Zebra and the Yellow Van

Written by Philip Elias
Illustrated by John Steven Gurney

Scott Foresman

Is it a yellow jet?

Is it a zebra up in a

yellow jet?

It is not a yellow jet.

It is a yellow van.

Is it a little van?

 Is Zebra up in a little van?

It is not a little van.

It is a big yellow van.

Can three get in to the van?

Three can get in to the van.

The yellow van is here.

The van is at the  zoo.

We like the yellow van.

We like Zebra and the

yellow van.